The Story of Christmas

by
VIVIAN FRENCH

illustrated by
JANE CHAPMAN

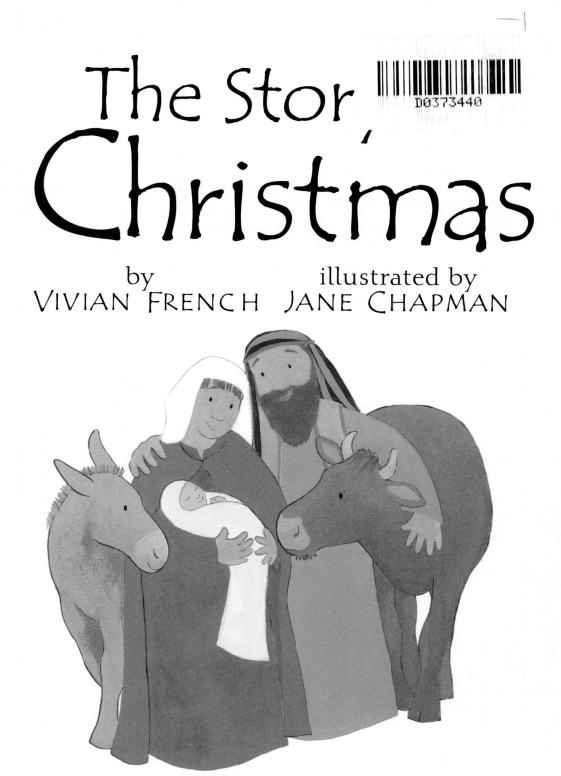

SCHOLASTIC INC.
New York   Toronto   London   Auckland   Sydney
Mexico City   New Delhi   Hong Kong

A long time ago God called for the angel Gabriel and gave him a very special message to deliver. God told Gabriel to go to a city called Nazareth and find the house where a young woman called Mary lived.

When Mary saw the angel, she
was frightened, but Gabriel told
her not to be afraid.

"God has sent me," he said. "God
has chosen you to be the mother
of His baby. He will be a wonderful
baby, and his name will be Jesus."

Mary was surprised, but
she smiled at the angel.
"I'm happy to do whatever
God wants," she said.

Mary had promised to marry
a carpenter called Joseph. Joseph
heard that Mary was going to have
a baby, and he began to worry
about what he should do.

God knew that Joseph was worrying, so He sent an angel to visit him. When the angel arrived, Joseph was fast asleep, so the angel slipped into Joseph's dream.

"Don't worry any more," the angel told him. "This is God's baby, and when he is born you are to call him Jesus."

Mary and Joseph were waiting for
the baby to be born when an order
came from the emperor.

Everyone was to pay him some
money. It didn't matter if they were
old or ill or even if they were about
to have a baby—the emperor said
they must go at once to the city
their family came from
to make the
payment.

Joseph's family came from Bethlehem, so he and Mary had to pack their things and leave Nazareth.

As it was nearly time for the baby to be born, they traveled very slowly along the road to Bethlehem.

When Mary and Joseph reached Bethlehem, they found many other people there. Grandfathers and grandmothers, uncles and aunts, fathers and mothers, and sisters and brothers and cousins—everyone had come to pay the emperor the money he wanted.

All the places to stay were full. Mary and Joseph knocked on every door, but the answer was always the same—no room, no room. The only place they could find was a stable, where the animals were kept.

While they were there, the baby Jesus was born. Mary wrapped him carefully and laid him in a manger full of soft hay.

The stable was not very far from some fields where shepherds were looking after their sheep. It was night time, and very dark, but suddenly the sky lit up. High above them was an angel surrounded by light. The shepherds were very scared, but the angel told them not to be afraid.

He said, "I bring you the
most wonderful news! Tonight in
Bethlehem the savior of the world
is born!" And he told the shepherds
how they could find the baby, safely
wrapped and lying in a manger.

Then, just as suddenly as the first
angel had come, the whole sky
was full of angels singing. They
sang "Glory to God in the highest,
and on earth peace and good will
toward men."

When the angels had flown back into heaven, the shepherds rubbed their eyes.

"Let's go to Bethlehem!" they said. "Let's go at once!"

And they left their sheep and hurried off to look for the stable.

There they found Mary and
Joseph, and the baby lying in the
manger, just as the angel had said.

It wasn't only the shepherds who wanted to see the baby Jesus. A long way away three wise men saw a star in the eastern sky. They knew it was a sign that someone very important had been born, and they followed the star until it came to rest above the stable.

The wise men came inside and saw Jesus with his mother, Mary, and bowed down. They gave the baby presents of gold and sweet-smelling spices called frankincense and myrrh.

And up above the stable all the
angels sang as the star shone down.
The Son of God was born.

For Marcus and Sally
with love
V. F.
For George David
J. C.

ISBN 0-439-22750-X

Text copyright © 1999 by Vivian French.
Illustrations copyright © 1999 by Jane Chapman.
All rights reserved.
Published by Scholastic Inc., 555 Broadway, New York, NY 10012,
by arrangement with Candlewick Press.
SCHOLASTIC and associated logos are trademarks and/or registered
trademarks of Scholastic Inc.

12 11 10 9 8 7 6 5 4 3 2 1   0 1 2 3 4 5/0

Printed in the U.S.A.   08

First Scholastic printing, September 2000

This book was typeset in Calligraphic Bold.
The pictures were done in acrylic paint.